for Mitzi and Jack
with best wishes and so many
thanks for bothering to know
the tinker who wrote the book.

Patrick
of the Hills

Poems for the Children of Scotland

by

Patrick Gordon-Duff-Pennington

Patrick of the Hills

Arena Press
An imprint of Arena Broadcast
Crag House Farm
Wasdale
Cumbria CA19 1UT

Author Photograph by Eric Robson
Cover Design by Ian Scott

Computer typeset in Adobe Garamond by
ASAT Productions

Printed in Great Britain by Sovereign Press

ISBN 0 946812 01 2

First Impression 1998
Second Impression 2011
Third Impression 2013

For two honorary godchildren
Lorraine Alexander and Isobel Currie
and their parents who brought them up to be
caring people
in an often careless world.

Patrick Gordon-Duff-Pennington was a revolting child brought up in Morayshire. He was educated at Eton College where he learned to translate the local paper into Latin and Greek verse and many other bad habits. At Trinity College, Oxford his dislike of authority increased partly because he wanted to be Foreign Secretary and his tutor Tony Crosland took the vacancy. Having been a shepherd on farms in Perthshire and Invernesshire he married Phyllida and moved to Muncaster Castle on the edge of the Lake District where he looked after his father-in-law's sheep. He loathed the place and swore never to return. He still leaves there. He farmed in Dumfriesshire, became Honorary President of the Scottish National Farmers' Union, Convenor of the Scottish Landowners' Federation, was awarded the OBE for services to rural Scotland and for some inexplicable reason has been Cumbrian Personality of the Year. For many years he was Managing Director of the family estate at Ardverikie in Invernesshire and in 1993 was appointed Chairman of the Deer Commission for Scotland. He deserves to be dead but hasn't quite made it.

Contents

The Scribes and the Pharisees

I saw old Andrew
Late last night, across the dyke,
Sitting with eyes that did not see.
Jessie had died last May,
His wife of many years
And now there seemed no point
In anything.
Even the dog, his constant friend
Could not ameliorate the loneliness,
So night after night he sat
Above the burn in quiet despair,
Endlessly watching with eyes that did not see
The primrose banks and breaking leaves
On the birches, and the hazel catkins
Casting their pollen on the evening wind,
While I, each night,
I passed along the other side.
He listened, but no longer heard
The curlew call,
Which could not hush his grief.
Long, long ago at darkening
He used to stand among his cattle
Or the lambing ewes,
Watching the rising moon across the hills
In dignity, but now
With Jessie gone, the family away,
He did not care,
And what did I do, who have so much,
I passed along the other side.
For years he'd watched
While urban votes
Elected governments which told him what to do,
Till now the law's an ass which states
The smells of cattle dung and sheep and pigs
Are not acceptable to urban refugees,
So one by one his liberties to farm the land
Were stripped from him.
His desk was full of littered forms
He never had been trained to understand enough

Patrick of the Hills

To wend his way across the bureaucratic maze
In search of subsidy.
His self respect was gone,
Stolen by you and me.
He only knew the life he used to lead
Before was right.
Often he'd worked alone
But now he'd had to learn
The meaning of true loneliness
Without a hope.
He thought he'd failed.
He owed the bank a lot.
They told him all his values
Had been wrong,
His care for stock misplaced,
His pride in work.
They told him, who had farmed his land
With loving care for years and years,
Society did not need him now.
Society only wished to pass along the other side.
So now this morning, as I went to work,
I found him, Andrew,
Dead from carelessness of you and me,
Drowned in the Ruskich burn,
Only the dog beside him in his grief.

Sketch for a Christmas Carol

Ended my year, ended my day of dreams,
Tomorrow again to face the world's beginning;
But tonight the world is waiting, and I,
I watch the endless miracle of the heavens
With the stars tumbling around the sky
Being shuffled by angels' wings
In a riot of celebration,
Lighting the eyes of my favourite cow,
New calved in the corner
Under the dyke.

Across the field, the breath of the sheep
Is lit by the moonlit shafts of light
Reflected from hoar frost trees
Standing in sheltered peace tonight.
I watch with crook gripped firm
In freezing work-worn hands
Talking to the beasts
And the owl in the sycamore tree,
Humming to the hedgehog asleep
Deep in its pile of leaves;
Learning a new celebration
Of the birth of the infant Christ
In a landscape miles away
Surrounded by other shepherds, while I,
Encircled by trusting animals wait
Under this northern sky.

Home of Lost Causes -
Thoughts of an old Oxford Blue on the
Establishment

I only went to Oxford
But that was just because
My mother had high hopes for me -
A fairly hopeless cause.

I've been a party chairman.
I've propped the NFU.
I've partly owned a castle,
And farmed a field or two.

But deep inside I'd much prefer
To find a different place
That understands irreverence,
From which I can't escape.

It clings to me tenaciously,
The wish to dig a pin

Patrick of the Hills

In any set establishment
Which thinks it's sure to win.
I do not like the Tories,
Dislike the Labour Left,
The SDP and Liberals,
Of policies bereft.

So because I'm always guaranteed
To say what can't be said,
I think I'd better stick to being -
An anarchist instead.

A Pair of Grey Wagtails Outside My Office Window

If I could have my needs fulfilled
I would retire
And maybe write a song or two,
And marry you,
But as it is
I have to balance books,
Plant flowers occasionally,
Have conversation with the public
In the afternoons,
Making pretence of happiness
Until that distant date that's undefined
When I am free to come to you.
I sit in offices. Outside my own
I watch a pair of grey and yellow wagtails line their nest
Across the yard, envying them
For all the silent certainty of spring.

Meantime, we have to wait
Till we can imitate those birds
And show off shamelessly
Before we sleep,
Knowing each night can be as long
As we decide to make it,
Shaping our lives as perfectly as wagtails' eggs.

The Peregrine

You are the lucky bird who lay
So wounded when the wicked wires
Ripped through your wings
Wiping your anchor shape,
Your piercing eye
Out from that wide free space
You always owned.

They brought you here,
Enclosed you in a convalescent cage,
Stitching your severed skin,
But fearing they would have to leave you
As an invalid.

The days you spent
As captive on your little perch,
In contemplation of dead chicks
Did not deceive you, never meant
More than an isolated interlude behind
An unaccepted barricade.

I too, have thoughts like yours,
But lacked all valid hope
Until I watched you on that day
We let you go again,
A steel grey scimitar
Which tore across the world
Of waiting sky.

It taught me how to find the faith
That you had always had;
The sure belief that one day, too,
For me
The freedom urge would break the bars
That hold me from my mountain winds.

"They Told Me, Heraclitus . . ."

I should have known today, my friend,
That you were moving out
Along the path that leads
Among the hills of sparkling stars,
For yesterday I stood beside the loch,
Looking across the waters as the evening came
To places where we used to go at lambing time.
They have all changed, I know,
But underneath the form
Of hillsides where we went to work
The rocks are just the same as those we used to touch.
The wind blows up at darkness still,
And sometimes snow;
The daffodils outside the bothy door
In spring, still bloom.

This year the deer are very slow in breaking out,
But late last night I stood beside the silent loch,
Listening to the roar of stags at dark.
Tonight they were completely silent and I should have known
That you were moving out.
You will be missed, but all the hills
You taught me long ago to know and navigate
Are full of memories,
And one day soon, we too,
Will follow up the path you took today
Among the pastures of the stars we watch tonight,
Learning from you once more a little differently
To swear at non-conformist dogs
And gather sheep.

*On the death of Neil Usher in 1990 aged 86. Hill farmer,
raconteur, friend, employer and adviser who taught me about
sheep and the hills and greatly influenced my life.*

Ships That Pass In the Night

It wasn't fair
The way God sent you out
Into my ageing world
Early in spring
This year -
You,
As part of the hills I love,
Part of the land I know,
Part of the bursting buds
That break like hearts
Upon the springtime trees.
It wasn't fair
That you should hold in you
All the caring of things I mind about,
And your voice
And your way of looking
Which told me you see
The world in the way
That I do.

It wasn't fair
We had so little time to put
Into that short, short snatch of life
All of ourselves
Only to know what we have to know,
Two ships passing
Across the island seas
Into some distant opposite
We were never destined to reach.
So now, for me,
All that is left
Is memory
Of something fine in the meeting
Of us.
It wasn't very fair
Of God.

The End of September

There was weeping at the hearth
In Lewis this night once more -
Two lives wasted and two men drowned
Under the vicious waves
With the tangle of seaweed around their limbs,
All for the sake of what?
Just one bloody lobster,
And the salt of the tears of the women
In tomorrow's porridge!

One of the two, father and son they were,
Calum, the son, promised to a young bride,
Pledged to the doctor's daughter,
And they to make their lives on the island.
Now, nothing remaining to show
Save the photo of him with his Glasgow degree
On the chest, and the thought of new life
That they might together have brought
Once more to a house at Marbhig,
With the children they'd hoped to rear
And now never will.
Gone, too, the other, Donald Iain, the father.
If there's hating to do
Let the strangers like me
Be those who must learn to hate
On your own behalf,
The endless demands of the sea,
So calm only a day ago
Under September sun,
With the sea birds cry at the darkening.
While you,
You in your grief,
Must turn your face to tomorrow and smile
At the joy of once knowing the two who are gone.
Hold them still in your thoughts
But leave it to me,
Who have loved, but not understood
The love of the merciless sea,
Blessed though I've been
With the kiss of an Island girl, your kin.

Leave it to me, the cursing and swearing
And you who are
The family to whom I can never belong,
Leave me to my fate
To curse the God of the sea
On behalf of your anger and grief.

*Most of the crofting families of Lewis have close links with the
sea. They have seen their inshore fisheries raped and the
essential income they provided destroyed, yet disasters are still
repeated as this one in 1996.*

Second Sight

I went back to Marbhig today
And Duncan, my girl's brother,
Was gone.
Marbhig is empty without him,
Without the sound of his voice,
And his humour;
The fish gone from the Minch
And the nets no longer outside the house
By the inner bay.
I watched as the tide covered the rocks
At the evening, but Duncan was gone,
And I was sad —
Sad for my girl at the lateness of the hour;
Sad for myself for the loss
Of one more shaft
Of a tiny islet of light
In the back of her smiling eyes;
But glad I was to be there,
Late though the time,
To be able to lay my hand on her arm,
And give her what strength I had
As we watched the moonpath, reached
Across the night time sea,
To wherever we have to go;
And I thought, next time,
It may be me!

Address at the Prize Giving of the East of Scotland Agricultural College

You are entering
The agricultural industry
At a time
Of utmost difficulty
The media will accuse me
Tomorrow morning
Of gloom - and doom!
They always have.
I call it realism.
The agricultural ministers (et al)
Call it a time of opportunity,
The dawn of some prosperity
Unheard before -
A time to do your neighbours down!
But you
Should never let them think
Your thoughts for you.

We have lived through times
Of constant revolution,
Your grandparents and I,
We've heard it all before!
The workforce on the land is still
Going down and down;
The average age of farmers, 56.
When I joined up
My pay was just a pound,
Which kept me happy -
And in chocolate once a week.
We lived like pigs
Without electric light
And God! We were happy
Milking cows by hand
And gathering sheep.
We stooked the corn
We sometimes had to cut with scythes,
And bind by hand.
We pressed the thistle prickles
From our fingers.

Sowed fertiliser out of sheets;
Hoed turnips; learned what blisters are,
And raked the hay
Gathered with tumbling Tom
Behind the horse;
We scaled the lime with shovels
Following the cart;
Learnt to observe our stock.
Not technically trained, like you
We lived on basic common sense,
Taught by our dog
Some sort of extra sensory
Intelligence.

First lambing on my own
I was so little trained,
My wife sat on the head
Of the reluctant ewe,
Reading instructions
From Home Doctoring of Animals,
While I soon found
The little brutes were all mixed up
In some way
Not quite illustrated
In the text.
We learned quite fast
What not to do
So now
After my years and years
Of teaching students
What moves to make at lambing time,
Seeing how difficult
They sometimes found the work,
I realise that
There is no substitute
For life's experience.

Untaught,
We ran up debts,
Forgetting one and one make two.
Escaped the banker's clutch by luck
And watched the vast majority

Patrick of the Hills

Of our contemporaries
Make just the same mistakes as us
And yet,
We tilled the stony ground,
Learning that acid soil needs lime,
Finding the way to live in harmony
With stock and season.
We groomed the cattle after tea
Each night,
Feeding them sometimes
Seven times a day,
And once the vet
In dinner jacket dressed
Helped us to calve a lazy cow.

We smelt - I expect,
Sometimes of silage,
Sometimes of dung, or pigs
And yet, and yet,
We learned to forge
That sympathy between
Man and his animals,
And land
That modern farmers tend
Too often to forget.
Whatever your professors say
True understanding is an art
You cannot learn from books.

My friends, I wish you luck,
And better manners
Than I ever learnt,
And if you want your father
To pass his farm to you,
I tell you,
From my vast experience,
The very wisest way
Is just to persuade your mother
To do your business for you
When she takes
The surly brute to bed!

For the Children of Scotland

I look at the sad faces in the street
And wonder what we're doing
Seeing the children returning from school.
We cannot give them cash,
And, even if we could,
It wouldn't do them any good.
There are few jobs,
And the parents have lost their way,
Misled by being told
That silver is the only star
To lead them into paradise.
We never gave our time enough
To tell the children's stories
The Island women told to us.
Let us now turn
From the modern gods
And find them a polished stone
From the edge of the loch,
Making a time to teach them
Before it becomes too late,
That sometime, somewhere soon,
For Scotland, there can be
More than a bitter yesterday.

For the Children of Kazminsky

The world we used to know is dead
Among the hills and fields
Where we were young,
So now
We have to travel all these many miles
To find the faith we had so long ago,
Not in the eyes of the children
Of our own land,
But in the faces and hearts
Of the young people of Russia
Who seem to have learnt so well

To love the earth
For which so many of their grandparents
Had died.
Because of all these children we have met
We shall go back to our own place
In search of the old beliefs
Which their smiles and songs
Have revived in us;
And when it is May 9th again
We, too, shall remember
The people who left this village
To fight to protect it.
So it was that yesterday,
In gratitude,
We laid our flowers
Below their names,
In remembrance, not only for you,
But for us
And the children
Of our own country.

*On a visit to a co-operative in the Northern Caucasus in
1988. Few people in Britain understand the appalling
suffering of the Russian people under Stalin and the extent of
their losses during the war with Germany. The care they took
of the children in the kindergartens showed how greatly they
valued their future.*

Mandarin Ducks in the East End of London

At dusk I wandered
Through the streets
And saw some sets
Of Chinese pots
Among the lots
In dusty shops
In Camberwell.

The paintings on them
Told the tale

Of happy life
With duck and drake
Beneath a tree;
Snowladen plum
Blossom for purity;
Tree paeonies for grace,
And love, and spring;
Chrysanthemums for autumn,
And for summer
All the pink tinged petals
Of the lotus blooms,
In the moonlight bright
Which guides the flight
Of August night
Through Peking skies.
Some Chinese king commissioned them,
And here they sit
Beyond the reach of fowlers' guns
Among the junk of centuries,
Unwanted lots
In dim-lit shops
In Camberwell.

On the Writing of English

Ages ago they taught me how to write
With elegance, grammatically precise.
Never start sentences with "but", "however",
So nowadays when civil servants send
Me papers, often rather hard to comprehend
With paragraphs which start "however";
When reams and reams of paper pulp
Come shooting through the letter box
Each day, you'll understand I get depressed.
They've never learnt the need for brevity
And waste so many words, so many trees,
To make a simple point
In ways that ordinary people
Rarely understand.

The Whitehall Civil Service

Determined to maintain the status quo
A solid barrier between the governed
And the governors
Who understand too well
The mechanism of the paper chains
Which they create.
Well, we, the common people now revolt
Against
  committees,
      memoranda,
         meetings,
            paper work,
               we do not want,
And taxes - none of which we understand!
Because the far - and far from civil Civil Service have designed
A system they made sacrosanct
In tablets of cement.
George Brown got drunk,
But managed to expose them.
We, too, have had enough!

It's time for most of them to go.
They have reduced the people to a nervous wreck,
Curtailed our liberty,
Forgotten Runnymede.
Just give them all a knighthood now,
And make them governors of coral isles
They once forgot to cross off from the list
Of Britain's old imperial inventory.
Tell them - "Get out!"
And we'll get on
Quite happily without their help,
Using our common sense
To save the time and money that we've spent
On them, for more essential things -
Like job creation, houses, food, and making love,
And sleep.

*John Bradbury of MAFF who supported the farmers of
Cumbria beyond the call of duty during the Chernobyl crisis
of 1986.*

Nightmare Ticket at MAFF

If Packer was paired with Portillo
They'd make the most virulent duo.
That MAFF would survive
Would be hard to contrive
And one wonders what fate would befall us.
They'd privatise trees,
Import new disease,
Buy all of our milk from the Dutch.
They'd sack all their staff,
Give contracts to half,
And claim it was good economics.
Right winger rectitude,
Arrogant attitude
Shoulder to shoulder the Thatcherites stand;
They'd vandalise grants,
They'd subsidise France,
British farmers they'd dump on the midden,
And as we descended
They'd privatise hell,
And Heaven as well,
That unsavoury duo
Of Packer, square jawed,
Allied to the ghastly Portillo.

*Richard Packer, Permanent Secretary of MAFF and Michael
Portillo, tipped to become the next Minister of Agriculture.
The government was treating the Forestry Commission badly,
wishing to privatise it. My friends needed support - this was
the result.*

Karl Hawkins

Dear Karl,
Where the hell have you gone?
We were just about to be friends
When you upped and off,
Leaving us no address. I tried,
Truly I tried,

Patrick of the Hills

Directory Enquiries for Heaven
But they said there were a lot of angels
Up there called Karl, and anyhow
You might be ex-directory.
So I tried the same for hell,
Satan answered himself and said:
"Karl? . . . Karl? . . . Karl?!
Nothing in my computer here,
Didn't he leave another name?"
Hawkins, "Oh yes, there is a Hawkins,
Though he's been around a long, long time,
And his CV says he was a pirate,
But no, not another Hawkins."
So that's all right then -
We conclude you must have gone to heaven.
You'll be looking good in a long dress with a harp
Strumming a tune with old Archangel Gabriel,
And I hope you're laughing
Because it isn't very funny down here
Among the embers
Of Margaret Thatcher's unspeakable dream.

*Interviewed in bed in my pyjamas for Granada TV by Karl
Hawkins and Nell Butler, the Cabinet Secretary's daughter.
He was a man of great charm who died immediately
afterwards. A new friend lost too soon.*

Old Bess
(Read at the International Sheepdog Society Dinner)

There only was ever one dog for me
That met with my diffident dumb demands,
Who never would make me feel a fool
While ignoring my ignorant futile commands.

"Come bye", I said, "Come bye, you fool"
She'd slip away on the other hand.

I was confused, but she was not,
Speeding so swiftly across the land.
But still my faithful dog meant well
For she always knew what for me was best,
Dismissing my oaths in the midday air
As she fetched some ugly ewe to rest.

Right at my feet the sheep expired
And Raymond MacPherson, the well dressed guest
Who had come for his Sunday lunch that day
With the unrehearsed demo seemed strangely impressed.

I made a mistake and sold my dog,
Twelve hundred pounds, not a penny less,
Was the price that I asked, and the price that he paid
On that Sunday in June when I sold Old Bess.
He'd bought the dog and I was left
Without a paddle, away up the creek -
And the bitch's daughter, she broke my leg
In the steading that night when shedding the sheep.

She bit the policeman. She gripped the ewes,
And taught me refinements of how to swear,
And now daily, my God, I wish that Old Bess
Was again at my heel and still sitting there.

So if you have dogs that suit you as well
They're worth more cash than you ever can get.
For God's sake keep them beside you as friends
And don't you ever dare to forget-

A dog that will love you and work as well
Is a dog that you never, ever should sell -

Even to Raymond MacPherson!

The Deer In Winter - A Political Essay

These are my people,
The Children of the Mist,
Huddled here in the eye of the storm
With the flurries of snow
Blowing in circles
Around the encircling arms
Of the corrie,
About to be confused
Where no shelter is.

They are troubled, my children,
Feeling the first stirring
Of the calves in their wombs,
Waiting, endlessly waiting,
From autumn
Through the starvation of winter,
For the sunlight shafts
In the summer hills
To warm the heather hollows
Of the inevitable birthplace
In the month of June.

Just now their backs are wet
And the wind
Strikes like a killing knife
Through the shivering flesh.
These are my people
With whom I can identify
In the time of my trouble,
Having known better days,
Hoping for a better tomorrow,
And that tomorrow
May come soon.

For now, my people are like the deer,
Individuals huddled in a great herd,
Not knowing, not seeing
Any clear road,

But there are leaders of the tribe
Who will force their heads
Out of the still of the eye of the storm
And into the teeth of the wind,
Running faster and faster
To arrive more quickly
At the farther end of their affliction.

They have done it
Countless winters before
And there is no substitute
For experience,
But sometimes now
Even the leaders are lost.

The hinds and the last year's calves
Follow the flow of the herd
In the wake of the leading deer
Seeking the far end
Of the wind,
And the peace of the shelter
They must find
In their night of starvation.
These are my people
With whom I can identify,
Seeking the security
Of a more tranquil place,
The last wild creatures in my world.
Watching them, my children,
I know I, too, have a lesson to learn -
I, and my wildness.

The Needles of Naxos
(On looking at a 17th century embroidery from the Greek Islands)

Did God drop into your eyes,
As into mine,
The seeing
Of the blue Aegean?
And did you feel
As I then felt,
Touching the green and umber
Of the stitches
On the homespun ground?

Oh! You saw,
And I saw,
What all the others never saw!
The sweep of glinting sickle
In the sweating hands,
And bronzed and black-haired arms,
Binding the blue flowered flax
In sheaves, to make the linen
For the loving fingers
Of the needlewomen of Naxos,
Working their thread,
Seated on stools
Beside the sea.

Absence

If you weren't there
Where would I be
With no belief in God,
Or government, or me?
No place to put my thoughts
And visions
As I wander through the countryside
Or listen to the waves
Beside the evening sea.

Were you not there
My ear could hear no sound
And there would be
No place to yearn for
In the lonely dawn.
Robin would have no space
To drop his notes
Sitting among the branches
Of the weeping pear.
My heart would have no beat,
And I no quickening pulse
To hear the calling of the wind
Among the autumn grass
When stalking deer.
I could not bear to watch
The silver water under sky
While greylag geese return -
Without you there.

In the Glen of Weeping - a Pain in my Chest

As I went up the road today
On my way to the north
I felt the wings of the black bird
Flutter across my life
And knew there was a distinct possibility
I would never again
Watch Spring
Rush into bloom in a garden;
That at any time
The call might come
Which would separate us for a while.
If this were ever to happen
I hope you will know
I shall try to make a place,
However far away it has to be
Where you can come
Eventually.
Tonight I need you,
But you are not here
To say farewell.

Good Friday

What's the matter with me today?
I feel cross and unhappy with my life.
I suppose it must be
The east wind and too much to do,
With you so many miles away.

I shouldn't be like this -
The magnolias are beautiful just now,
And even the camellias are still
Flashes of blood red flame
Where some escaped the frost
On the edge of the wood
A week ago.

Though I
No longer go to church
I can't help thinking
On this day
Of all the sadness on another hill
Almost two thousand years ago.
I can't believe
The beauty of a garden such as this
Could have meant so much as it does to me
To the sufferers with the blood
Dripped from their wounds
Upon the earth beneath
At Golgotha.

Think of the awfulness
The world has since committed in His name.
The One in the middle
Who calls for his Father
On behalf of us all,
All of the time.
Think of the devastation
Of Humanity to which
The world has put His signature.
Think of brutality
Committed in religious wars.

Our sympathy should be addressed, maybe,
To those two common criminals
On either side of Him
For in their nameless names
The human race
Never committed itself to war
Or killing of their fellow men.

They, then as now, perhaps,
Stole, not having enough
To feed their children,
Not having enough to live upon.
Perhaps they are the ones
We should remember
On this day of trouble
After the prison riots
At Manchester.

Margaret Thatcher

I do not know
What you will think tonight
Before you sleep.
Perhaps you are a little sad
And certainly you must be very tired.
I, and my colleagues,
We did not always like
The things you said
Nor the clear acerbic way
You sometimes said them;
But tonight I have to write
Only to let you know
How much your courage and great heartedness
Has been an inspiration
To those like us
Who sometimes find themselves unarmed
On unfair battlefields
We know that no one could have fought
As hard as you

Patrick of the Hills

For what you thought was right -
Not out of selfishness,
But for your fellow countrymen.
For that you have the gratitude
And sympathy
Of one
Who often thought you wrong.

*On Margaret Thatcher's dismissal from power. Her ruthless
determination no doubt raised the status of Britain in the
world, but her unilateral imposition of the Poll Tax on
Scotland made the break up of the UK inevitable - I think!*

Johnny Sequoia

*Redwood, a tree, is sequoia sempervirens. Eucalyptus is a gum
tree. One who collects its sap is, presumably, a Gummer. John
Redwood, then Secretary of State for Wales treated Ian
Mercer, Director of the Welsh Countryside Council, a decent
man, with gross discourtesy.*

Oh, Johnny, Johnny,
Johnny Sequoia Sempervirens
Il fait s'en aller au Cabinet -
Which only means go to the loo
In French.
M4 to Wales and back again
To meet with Johnny Eucalyptus (Gummer)
While on the way reducing all the PPG's
To just a single sheet, recycled,
Of A4 tightly written — mind you,
It's not the sort of cycle that was meant
By Tebbit's "On your bike"!

Whatever you may wish
Your aim is admirable, though quite unpractical.
Redwood's your alias, without red corpuscles.
In true blue veins, you have
A Rolls Royce brain
Without a human heart;
A total lack of understanding

That countryside needs capital,
Needs mega bucks,
(Fatter by far than Lydney's fallow deer)
Which no amount of coaxing will extract
From a reluctant rural populace
That's strapped for cash
From Anglesey to Pontypool.
They do not share your dream
For Government of opting out
From using public funds
To help the Welsh environment.

Oh! Johnny, Johnny,
Johnny, Sequoia Sempervirens
Soon you'll be gone,
Flushed down the loo of history,
Nought but a nasty after-taste
In the mouth of a nation,
Losing a lung through lack of oxygen.

Johnny go home!
Your peerage will not come
For services
To Wales — not now,
Nor ever!

Kelburn Castle

Imprisoned spirit
In the sleeping house,
I hear you fighting
To escape the manacles
That hold you here,
Not knowing what you want,
But knowing well enough
You do not wish
To be dictated to
By centuries of stone
And protocol!

Sunday — Doing the Heritage!

Silent they go,
Looking at silver in the dining room
Only believing half
They hear me saying on the tape,
Good people coming to inspect the past,
Their laughter silenced out of misplaced reverence -
I really think they think
That they are trying to improve their minds
But life to live has more of levity than that -
I long to explode
The hanging silence of the Sunday afternoon
With just a subtle touch of not too reverend mirth.
Let's have a party, people,
Stop all this sombre silent cavalcade,
Putting an end to what has seemed
My endless afternoon,
Tying loose ends in silence as I sit
Fidgeting
In the dining room.

From Nepal

I have tramped the villages of high Nepal,
Seen Everest's far snows
Blue in the morning moon;
Slept by the fire
Under the stars on terraces,
And counted skeins of snow geese passing by
Over towards Makalu.

I have heard
The deep notes of the horn players
At the mountain weddings
And watched the whirling of the quern
Spinning in the hands of the children
At the house of the Chetri.

I have admired
Some of the attitudes of this mountain people
Who measure distances in time
Not miles. They question, though
They do not answer one,
Nor do they often smile.

But through it all, my heart
Is aching for Scotland
With its washing of grey waters
And its rocks;
Is waiting for
The calling of my children and
The softer speech and gentler eyes
Of my own people who
I love, and to whom I belong,
Even in this far place
So lost upon the rim of time.

On a visit to the Gurkha pension posts in eastern Nepal in 1970.

Address at Lara's Memorial Service

My love, I have no fire tonight
With you so far away!
No more I see my Clydesdale mare
With all the stars her huffing breath
Kindled each dawn from frosty air,
And sparks her silver shoes
Struck from the stony track
That led us long ago across
The morning on our way to plough.
My love, I have no longer fire!
And when dark comes
With nought but dreams
Her stall will still be empty there -
No rustling of the shuffled straw
Around her feathered legs;

Patrick of the Hills

No sound of munch contented as
She eats her evening feed,
And I shall have to sit alone tonight,
Setting my memories as snares
To try to catch the sound of geese
Sweeping in V's across the moonlit sky
Beyond the distant Firth that once
Was home, but now my ears grow deaf,
My eyes no longer bright
With you so far across the years,
And far too far away to light
The candle on the window sill
To guide me home at darkening.
My love, I have no fire tonight.

*Address at a memorial service at St Columba's Pont Street
which reduced the congregation - and me - to tears.*

For the Women of the Scottish Countryside

Women of Scotland, has it come to this?
We are ashamed; the land has been raped.
"Forgive us our debts", you said in your Sunday pews,
Your men coerced by the need to survive.
They tell us: "You're businessmen now",
But we don't understand what the nation wants.
We're bitter, confused, and mere machines,
Divorced from the caring earth
That our fathers taught us to tend.
'They' accuse us of everything under the sun,
But the sheep you helped us to lamb last spring
No longer pay for the rent.
Next year the yields of our grain will drop.
The soil lies sour, deprived of the lime
We cannot afford to buy.
We were not trained to farm like this.
Although just now the silage pits are filled,
The grain bins full,

There is no cash to stock the cattle courts this year,
While up the hill the autumn sales
Make poor return for one year's work
Under the mountain skies.

Not having paid attention to our sums
We've been misled — or worse, not led at all,
By urban politicians
With macro-economic dreams,
Advised by well-paid men without responsibility
With little knowledge of our maintenance costs.
They juggle with our lives.
Meantime they can't decide, and we,
We don't know what to do.
Their game is power for which
We do not care, but can't ignore.
Their insults hurt.
"You must be rich, who farm the land",
The urban majority say,
Knowing quite well the land cannot be sold.
They seem to want, in their uncertainty,
A poppy here, a pine tree there -
Easy for them to talk
Who do not have to live their lives
Placed in financial tourniquets
They can't control.

The swallows did not nest
Beneath the cartshed eaves this year.
Our luck has gone away,
So when the spring creeps up the glen again,
Some of our friends may not be there,
But you, wise women of the Scottish countryside,
Who bore us, and cursed us,
And loved us and mended our socks,
It's you who will need to be there
When the geese go north on the April wind.
It's you, only you, who can love us enough
To teach us once more
The need for the care of our land,
And return us our self respect.

State of the Union Message (1989)

They do not understand, those Unionists,
Sitting in London clubs or Parliament.
It's they who've sold the nation short,
Who cannot comprehend
The reason for the fighting talk
Of young men with no job to do
In bars of west coast pubs
On Friday nights.

Too many absentees
Have used their highland house
As cheap hotel,
Dreaming up dreams of self
As some philanthropist.
They thought, in arrogance
They only had to pay the wages,
Not waiting to listen
To the natives' needs.

So now,
Young men, and women too,
Well filled with alcohol
And out of work,
Wish to design a future for themselves
Without allegiance to a far-off government.
Seeking a target for their odium
They work out sums that don't add up
And call it freedom,
Blaming the English, dreaming dreams,
Lost in a haze of whisky fumes.

Reason dictates
There has to be another way
Than total independence,
Where Scotland takes decisions nearer home.
We need investment, but we need a voice
More obvious than the one we have,
And ears that sense
The aspirations of the fellow citizens.

We need a clearer vision
Of where the Nation ought to go.
"Two acres and a cow" is not enough,
But the Unionists must remember
Their days of doubtful reasoning
Are done.

Station Hotel — Not Inverness

Sitting, waiting -
A child of a lost generation in the lounge,
Watching the ghastliness of modern life pass by.
Women in spotless white jerseys
Bought in the knitwear shops,
Bottoms too big by far
For scarlet trousers tight
Which emphasise their ugliness.
Two old guests paying their accounts
And a loud-voiced man in shirt sleeves
Asking for a glass of water and an aspirin
For a migrained American wife
Upstairs.

Gone, gone
Are the men with grey moustaches
And Highland Brigade ties;
Gone are the mothers and the wives
In family tartan skirts
And sensible shoes.
No one I know.
The breakfast was disgusting with
Synthetic sausages;
Marmalade with the taste of peppermint
In plastic trays;
And the eggs tasting
Of fried fish from the night before.

Lost among the modern decor and
The awfulness of modern life

Patrick of the Hills

I sit — and wait!
This, which was once a flavour of the Scotland
That we knew
Is now no more than a gross irrelevance
To the life of the people -
A tiny space from which
Those from another planet can return
Thinking the unthinkable,
Telling their neighbours
That they have "done"
Scotland!

Real Cool!

Mary Packard, Secretary of San Francisco Opera, who used to visit Muncaster once a year.

Mary Poppins
Flew in from San Francisco today,
Tall, elegant, beautifully dressed,
And in no time at all
She has restored this maddening place
To sanity.

I like
Mary Poppins
Who is everybody's friend,
And who comes back
Like a gentle wind
Each spring.

As soon as she's gone, no doubt
We will return to our awful normality,
But for today
She makes everybody feel
A little less mad.
And a little less annoyed
At being alive.

Mary Poppins
Is real cool!
That's what I think!

For my God-Daughter — Lucy Carrigan

Dearest Lucy,
You know they say
That life begins at sixty or so.
Well, don't you believe them!
I was sixty last week,
And it's plain not true.
My bones ache as I doze at night
And my body is slow and old,
But deep in my heart I feel just the same
As the year I was twenty-two.

My eyes can still see the beautiful land
When I run in my mind
As I used to do.
Watching with kindly eyes as bright
As the yearling colts in your father's fields,
Chasing the shadow of racing clouds
Across the mat of the sweet green turf,
As they're swept by the south-west breezes
From the slopes of Slievenamon.

I can still look at a graceful girl
And wish I was young again,
For all of my sixty summers or so -
And I bet your father's the same -
But the years have laid hands
On my aching limbs
As I sit by the smoking fire,
So I'll have to search
For a nice young man
To take you to Dublin Show next year,
But never regret, and never forget,
The years of your youth that are past;

While I, I shall wish
That the straight young man
Waiting for you at the edge of the ring
Was the eager youth
That I used to be once
Those thirty-eight Dublin summers ago.

John Coutts and the Generous Fish

I seed some searchin' beady eye
Refleckit in the gin clear autumn water —
Ma Goad! It's Coutts!
I thocht I 'd seen the laist o' him
As loon o' echt yair owd,
A hirplin' thro' the August grass
Beside some burn near Brig o' Dee.
Ma mooth was sair thon day
From some wee hook
He'd droppit wi' a wurm impaled
Thro' swirl o' froth, wi' burn in spate.
But fate is aft times nae sae guid
To likes o' me who lives sae lang,
So noo he's back, a man retired
And I a monster fush.
And "ouch!", his bluidy hook,
That catched me once, has catched me twice,
The great cock fush that's me,
Who's swum and swum
Acrost the salty sea and back,
I'm sure it's mair than fufty times
Till noo it's certain sure I am
The biggest fush that ever swam.

I thocht I'd seen the laist o' him,
That tinker loon I'd long forgot,
But noo ah'm deid upon the bank,
The muckle fush frae Brig o' Dee,
And I, who's mair than twice his size,

Echt hunnert pund — I'll break his scales!!
You see, I did not reckon then
The big hert that the wee man had,
For fortune dealt him several blaws
That a' thro' life he owercame.

I wis careless, I wis free,
But he, he workit on an' on,
The canny man, the wily man
That spent his youth near Brig o' Dee.
While I, I'm doon in Hell recht noo,
Keepin' the Deil company.
Too big for Mary's fryin' pan,
Too big to carry doon the street
To sell in Wallet's Auction Mart,
John Coutts, he's sure to last forever,
To catch a thousan' careless fush.
I have to say perhaps, mebbee,
The wee mon has desairved his rest,
But rest for him means none for fush
Betwixt Urr's mooth, Dee's mooth
And Brig o' Dee.
And when he's done wi' catchin' them,
Sitting in heaven at God's recht hand,
Perhaps he'll say "Amen" for me,
The stupid fush
Who never lairned at primary school
It's none too safe to tangle wi'
A man who's freends wi' a' the fairmers,
Who let him dig in stinkin' middens
For wurms to catch
The likes o' me!

Sae guid luck Coutts,
You death o' me -
I ken a bonny fechter noo -
If you've survived sae mony yairs
The girning o' you fairming freends.
I guess you've earnt a puckle rest.
I'm no the fairst, and no the last
Puir fush to lay upon the grass,

The victim of your rod and line.
But man and fush, I'm sure baith say,
"Coutts is the soundest man we ken".
Sae guid luck, Coutts, you wise old man,
Who caught the biggest fush that swam,
Bigger than ony dream you had,
Droppin' your hook among the eddies
That fatal day you first met me
When jist a loon at Brig o' Dee.

Like a' guid fush and fushermen,
I really think ma tale is true -
Ma heid's sae big, ma bulk sae heavy
I'd top the sales of suckled calves
At ony time in Wallet's Marts.

A mite confused twixt fly and worm.
A mite mixed up twixt Urr and Dee,
Such cocktail's nothing like a lie — like me -
But itherwise ma tale is true -
The biggest fush that ever lived,
The biggest fush that ever took
John Coutts' muckle feathered hook.
I'm doon in hell, but a' the same
I canna' help but wish him weel,
The guid wee lad frae Brig o' Dee.

Ruth From Maryburgh

She sits behind the desk
With her crown of dark hair
And her smiling voice -
Only a receptionist, she said -
Dealing out tea and justice
To the customers
At Radio Highland.

Early morning outside
In Culduthel Road

With the birds singing
In the quietness
As though there had never been
Spring before
In Inverness.

In the cool place
Which is a model
That other BBC offices
Should emulate
The victims about to be interviewed
Are calmed by the charm
Of Ruth
From Maryburgh.

Ruth Henderson, aged 19, a perfect example to the Birtian axemen of the BBC.

A Fresh Young Graduate From the Nature Conservancy Council

I wish to designate your land, - she said
Why? I said
Because she said,
You don't know how to use it!
For whom? I said.
For the nation she said,
But my first duty is to keep a roof over my wife's head,
And food in my children's mouths,
And, anyway, there are two nations -
Added to which, I paid for my land!

But I
Went to university.
I have a degree.
I know! She says.
Who says?
I do, added to which
I'll give you money if you do as I say.

But it doesn't make sense, I said.
It's the law — she said!
Oh! That!!
Anyhow, you'll be paid for doing what I want,
And doing as I say.
When? I said,
Looking at my cash flow.
ASAP and if it's not as soon as that,
Blame the Treasury — everybody else does!
But I don't want an SSSI.
What you want has little to do with it,
And you can only appeal to NCC -
That's me, she said.
A triple SI it is!
So I am left
Feeling resentful,
Wishing I'd never heard
A word like conservation!

The land will care for me
If I remember
All the old wisdoms that my father taught
Uncoerced and unseduced
By designations that he would
Never have understood.

Red Kite

What a way to end the year -
A puff of feathers poisoned
By alphachlorolose.
No more the proud wingspan,
Casting its fearful shadow
On the crouching mouse;
No more the glinting eye,
Catching the sea light of the firth
Beside its temporary hunting ground.
What lessons should we draw
From this unnecessary incident?

One — it was a most monstrous thing to do,
To let a foreign bird
Loose in a habitat
Unsuited to its needs.
Two — it was not Scottish courtesy
To Swedes for any man
To kill their generous gift.
And three, above all, three,
The mortal man
In all of us must learn
To live in harmony with natural things
Or in the end
Man will destroy himself.
This is no time
To ask for licensing
Of alphachlorolose.

Alphachlorolose is a poison once widely used to kill crows.

Message from the Hills and Islands 1980

I have seen the living of the people destroyed,
Sacrificed on the altar of urban democracy
By the ignorance of well-meaning politicians.
I am not bitter but I am so sad
To have seen small business broken everywhere
In the sacred name of progress -
Their word, not mine -
Or the fight against inflation.
I read one day, a year or two ago,
Of the Minister of Agriculture
Floating through South America
Saying to the Uruguayans, the Argentinians
"Send us your lambs
And do not worry. We will eat them!"
We already have too many,
And so the people in the hills die out -
In the holy name of progress.
I have seen men encouraged to improve their land

Broken on the wheel of their improvements.
I have watched people trying to give employment
Forced to lay off their men.
I have heard schoolteachers preaching
That life on the land is bestial,
Poorly paid and not to be pursued.
So now
The young ones sneer
At the lost knacks of country life
And a generation is absent from the hills.
Perhaps we should go back
To the virtue of each man giving a roof
Over the heads of his wife and children
With a fire in the hearth
From the peat and the birch trees,
And food.
If not — we die.

Donald's Message

For forty-three, almost forty-four years,
You have fed on the memory
Of the man you thought that I was
When I left home.
We were close, you and I,
After our father died, but I was no paragon of virtue
And I'm sorry I'm not there now
To tell you to pull yourself together.
Marty, you have a good brain which you haven't used.
All along you have kidded yourself that it is my memory
That makes you idle, and allows you to take advantage
Of the people who wait on you, hand and foot.
You trade on them, you know,
And it just isn't good enough,
So snap out of it!

You see,
I was no hero when, just like everybody else,
I had to join the draft.

They sent me to Honolulu.
We weren't particularly scared that day I died
In 1944.
After our briefing we climbed in the cockpit of the Avenger
Which had been loaded with its torpedoes
On the deck of the Enterprise.
The engines spun into life. We checked the
Gauges and took off.
It was another routine strike
To attack the enemy battle fleet.
We found them close to the Palau Islands.
The Japanese pom-poms opened up
As soon as we were in range,
And I could see the faces of the gunners
As determined to get me as I was to sink their ship.

The air was mad with gunfire
Coming at us from every angle.
There were planes falling out of the sky
Everywhere,
And it was clear there wasn't going to be
Much of a squadron left.
It wasn't a good place to be,
But I wasn't afraid and only had a job to do.
Suddenly they got me,
The plane hit the sea
And then I was dead.

You know
They say that we go to Heaven.
Well, it wasn't quite like that.
We understood the grief of those we left behind
And we were grateful to those who tried to remember us
At home, but Christ, Marty,
All this pretence of seeing us
Without any of the blemishes
You know, and we know, that we had
Gives us no peace.
So I'm sending this message to tell you
To give us a break.
All this stirring of memories gives me no sleep -

Only revives the thought of the Japanese gunfire
Which did for us, and the shock
Which ended our lives.
So, Marty, snap out of it.
Stop using me as an excuse
For not using your brain.
It is still not too late to stop wasting your life
In a selfish way, and to start
Thinking of other people now.
For Christ's sake, begin at the beginning again!

*On meeting a strange American, still grieving for her brother
after 40 years and making herself ill on account of it.*

Highland Region AGM - Scottish Landowners' Federation

We have been lucky
Who have learnt
Through years and years
Of culling deer and herding sheep
The magic of the Highland hills;
Hearing the wind on winter nights
Driving the snow in drifts
Across the barren land
And in beneath the doors of byres
Or through the dark arcades of pines.
Often we've watched the moon
Shed light across the loch
Going to far off meetings
An hour before the dawn.
We've learnt a consciousness
Of all that went before
And tried to use it for the benefit
Of those who needed homes and jobs -
And yet, go out
Into the streets of Inverness
You won't walk far

Before you find a man who says,
"Landowners are privileged parasites
Who rape our land,
Control the lives of whole communities
For whom they do not care one jot;
Seek to exclude
The people from the hills,
Plant trees to spoil the scenery.
Puncture the mountain bikes
By leaving stones about the hills;
Bully the government for private gain."

Some of you I have known
Since childhood days,
Fathers of others I served beside
Doing my National Service
In the Camerons.
Some of you have, from time to time,
Annoyed me quite immoderately;
Those who too often come
Out of necessity from far away,
Arrive exhausted from their city desks
Contributing little enough
To life in the communities
In which they live
A bare eight weeks a year.
Too often, they don't understand
The deep resentment of the native populace
Who sometimes hide their thoughts
Behind their Highland courtesy.
I try to represent you
In the fairest light I can
Through all of this and that,
But God! It's sometimes difficult.
I hope you understand the reason
That I cannot say I'll guard you
When you break the law.
The job of your convenor
Is to talk to politicians,
Often a little ignorant,
Quite hostile to the private ownership of land;

Patrick of the Hills

Led by the nose by conservationists
Who hardly ever have
To make a living from the soil coming from cities miles away.
He has to talk to civil servants
And the Press;
To all of them, on your behalf,
He has to try to put a smile
Of innocence and goodness on his face,
Even although the thoughts of some of you
Are sinister.

Of all of you
I do not always totally approve,
I know quite well, at most,
You sometimes don't approve of me.
At best, you merely think me mad,
And yet, you know that when I speak
I try to speak the truth
For you — and when I say for you,
I also mean the Scottish land.
To serve you is the greatest honour
I could have.

The times are difficult.
Our houses cost a lot to keep.
Our land still needs the care
It always needed,
But now the things it can produce
Cannot maintain the past
The way the past demands.

My forecast is
On some tomorrow we shall see
A parliament in Edinburgh *
We do not think we need;
A government in London, just as now,
For which we do not care,
For which we have a mutual disrespect,
With vicious councils here and there,
Peopled by men whose fathers were
Treated quite badly by an absent laird -

And on that day remember me
Because my job is now
To talk to everyone,
Trying to persuade them all,
Owning the land we own,
We have a part to play,
Not in the past
But for the people
Who depend on us.
Too often now land has become
No more than a commodity
To buy or sell,
But you know, and I hope
Our children know
The land needs love,
We do not own the land,
The land owns us,
But while I live
I'll fight my best for you
To prevent
The constant whittling of your rights
Which all the time is limiting
The contribution
That we can and ought
To make.

* *Written in 1990*

In the Eye of Ben Armine

At the falling of night
I will meet you by the raging torrent of the Blackwater.
Salmon will be leaping in the pools
And the first leaf fallen from the rowans,
Spinning in the frantic foam.
The crash of the falls will be the filling of our ears,
And our noses charmed by the myrtle scent,
Yet still,
Still in that land,
That seemingly smiling land,

Patrick of the Hills

The bogs will be full of the ghosts of the evicted men
And the plaintive bleat of the Cheviot sheep
Who displaced them in the affection of the lairds.
We shall be happy awhile but when we are gone
The hills will be filled once more with the tortured past,
And the minds of the men who were wronged
On the silenced greens
Those so many summers ago
In the eye of Ben Armine.

Dark Island

Why the hell
Did I walk
Into your life
Or you
Fall into mine?

I have nothing to give
Because I belong
To someone else,
And yet
On these wild nights
Your hand becomes
Something
I could not be
Without.
Steering through dark,
Across the Scottish hills
On nights without a moon
The consciousness
Of you being there
Is the
One steady point
Among the chaos
Of my life.

You do not go,
Or come.

Nor I to you,
But your fragrance
Pervades my thought,
Like flowers.
I offer nothing,
Ask for nothing,
But as the wind
Rattles the windows
Just before I sleep
You're always there
And I
Am terribly glad.
So when the storm dies down
I'll pick camellias for you,
Some pink, some white,
And in my mind
I'll put them in a little vase
Beside your bed,
Hoping to purge the sin
Of loving you -
Quite as much
As I do!

Give Them the Land

I stood with you beside me in my mind
Telling them how you'd whispered in my ear
"Give them the land!"
"It is not possible", they said
And all the lawyers in their offices
Will say "it's quite impossible"
Rubbing their hands with glee
At thought of yet another Act -
But mostly they don't understand
The meaning of the word "community".
They only understand the webs they weave
With words. They have no "vision",
Nor few lairds, about the ethics of the croft.
How crofting is not farming. How Angus MacRae

Patrick of the Hills

Would help his enemy in time of need;
How Angus Macleod has so much dignity.
If I were wounded in a battle
I would not hesitate to seek their help,
Knowing that they and all their womenfolk
Would freely give, and shelter me
As if I were their son.

They didn't even smile, those in the hall,
Exhausted by the rhetoric of yesterday.
Donald Macleod and his biblical delivery
And the onslaught of Alan Macrae, the Assynt man,
Whose words were barbed with unselected prejudice,
Risen from years and years of wrong.
"Take the land which is ours", they said
"Give us back our own" with all their eloquence,
But in my ears I heard a gentler message,
"Give them the land!" you'd said.
Yet they should smile for times have changed.
Now should be hour of healing in the crofting lands.
Not every laird is bad, not every crofter good,
But time has come
To raise our eyes from history
And set new sails into the shifting wind.

The land is theirs in all but name.
The land has paid no dividend
To those who, for too long,
Have sold the crofters' rights as chattels,
Without the courtesy of telling them
To whom their rent was paid.
Value to lairds has gone
From what they thought they owned.
Now is the time when many lairds
Who only come for holidays,
Sick of financial liability
Might say enough's enough,
Handing the crofters back their dignity.
The crofting lands must stay in crofting tenure,
But still the time is ripe for change.
Some there may be who say

"We're quite well off the way we are,
We do not want responsibility."
They should assume it now or else
Lay themselves open
To the accusation that they want to keep
Not only the land, but all the poison too
Of centuries of grief. They tell me "very nice,
But of course it can never happen."
I tell them that it can, and will,
Even if not in every township through the land,
Even if not tomorrow. We must start to talk,
Searching for points we can agree.

Don't they remember how Alistair Strathnaver
Sat with crofting representatives
To hammer out agreement
On the Crofter Forestry Act?
That was a start of something which
The cynics said could never pass.
How wrong they were!
So now let's try to untie all the knots,
Of bitterness.
That strangle crofting with its past.
The time is here to quiet the rhetoric
And say quite gently to the lairds
With all the inborn courtesy of Highlanders
And all the phrasing of the Gaelic tongue
"Give us the land!"
Awaiting their response may take some time,
And when it comes I may be gone,
But let them remember the lady from Marbhig
Who whispered in my ear,
And let them remember the Saturday morning in 1993
When the first pebble was flung into the pool,
And wait until another laird says it again and again,
Until the whisper becomes a roar
"Give them the land!"

Then you, my sweet, the whisperer -
You can be proud.

Beethoven

This is the very first time in my life
That I have really understood
The terrible affront
Beethoven must have felt
At his deafness
No longer able to listen
To the sound of the notes
He had written on the pages.
I feel alone, cut off from sound.
I remember that evening
The Russian tanks rolled into Prague
In 1968.
Menuhin was to play
The violin concerto in the Usher Hall.
Before he started he stood on
The platform and addressed the audience -
"On this dark, dark day,
A shadow of thirty years ago,
I wish to dedicate my performance tonight,
As did Beethoven his life,
To the great and indomitable
Spirt of man."
The audience were all in tears
And as the notes floated from his instrument
They spoke to everyone,
"There must be a God", they said.

For more than a month
I have not heard with ease.
I am sure it is only a temporary affliction,
But sitting in the surgery,
Where I write this,
Among the greyness of an early autumn day,
It came to me, the hopelessness he must have felt -
No song, no sound;
Able to see, only the noiseless notes
Upon the page.
How he could find the imagination
To continue to write,

Out of his head and heart,
Without his ear,
Must surely be a testament
To the greatness
Of God's gift to man.

If I Were Rich

If I were rich
At Christmas time each year
I'd buy a field of violets
Just for you,
And hand you my heart
For you to break
Among the fragrance
Of the purple blooms.

*For Bridget Kendall, BBC correspondent in Moscow, to whose
voice I used to listen on the World Service through eternities of
sleepless nights.*

The Highland Night

Lonely, at dusk, upon my Highland hill
I watched the skeins of wild geese flying south tonight
To winter estuaries
Driven by the tail of the Arctic wind
And the first dappling of snow
On the high tops.

The deer are down among the birch trees now.
Late in the afternoon I killed a stag
Not long with hinds,
High in the Bow Corrie of the Gealcharn.
It was cold and the deer making for the shelter
At the back of the hill.

Patrick of the Hills

As I went down above the forest gate
At the darkening.
There were the beginnings of frost,
With the Pole Star very bright on the other side of the loch
Above Creag Ruadh
Where a single stag was roaring.

The geese,
On their way south to where you are,
Unsettled me.
Here I have a job to finish.
In another six weeks the tups will be let out
And the first hinds hanging in the larder.
Only another twenty stags to kill
Before the end of the season,
Two weeks from now.

The hoggs have gone away for the winter
Into Strathdon,
All the lambs and the cast ewes sold.
But the geese remind me of the winter on its way,
Asking me, when I have finished
Will you still be waiting for me,
Far to the south,
To where the birds are stretching out their wingbeats
Through the night time sky.
Already their voices are fading into the darkness.
At this time I am drowned with fear
Of all the loneliness of you-not-there

Autumn is a depressing time
Now that we're not so young,
But I want you to know
That I am tied to you
With lines as strong
As all the instincts which will take the geese
Back to their breeding grounds again
In spring.

Anticipation of Friends

Soon it will be tomorrow and I shall see you!
I feel like some small boy
Anticipating something that he really wants to do -
Wandering with Nanny Munro
Up to Wellhill across the childhood ford at Moy;
Collecting the brown eggs
From under speckled hens in the well-strawed nesting boxes;
Riding home to the farm
In the cart behind the Clydesdales at the turnip time;
Eating fresh oatcakes and raspberry jam
Beside the kitchen fire before going home.
Now I am old and cynical,
And tonight my back aches as I sleep in the chair,
But tomorrow I shall see you again
Which makes everything all right -
Every time that it happens!

The Cumbrian Circle

Men so clever they stood on the moon;
Men on top of the highest mountain in the world;
And yet they return to Cumberland,
Just as the silver fish running in the rivers,
Making, once more, back to their beginnings
To spawn on the gravel redds of the beck
Where fish have always bred
Since the melting of the glaciers -
Crystal waters between hazel wands;
Woods filled with the wild garlic,
Daffodils and banks of primroses
In the Spring
Where the sunlight strikes through the breaking leaf buds
On the floor of the crystal stream;
Rivers running through the timeless fields
Herdwick ewes gathered from the fells for the lambing,
Searching for the non-existent green
Of the April grass.

Patrick of the Hills

The landscape changed
After the start of time
When the molten mountains settled
In their forms, and again, and again,
It changed with the ice,
With the glaciers smoothing the rocks
Of their origins.
Then came the trees
The graceful birches, and the oaks,
Reaching their roots down to the deep nutrients
Among the crevices of the rocks.
The seasons came and went a hundred, hundred times
Leaf fall after leaf fall.
Acorns dropping in the rotting mat,
Seeds of the birch blown on the autumn breeze
Among the fissures of the rocks,
To grow to make music
For the September wind,
Sighing among their leaves.

Out from the arms of the mountains,
All the time, the sea and the wind;
Waves breaking, backwards and forwards,
Backwards and forwards,
On the shifting strand.
The deer browsed the seedlings,
Followed by man the hunter,
Man the Hunter, following the tip
Of Orion's sword to the south above Black Combe
On December nights,
Struggling to survive.
Skins to keep warm, and a place to live
By the fire, the flowers of the flame of the fire,
Cut from the woods with his primitive tools;
Man surrounded by fire,
Safe from the beasts
And other more hostile men.
Later they came Romans and Danes, and a saint or two,
Among the unbelievers, and sometimes the Scots.
They tamed the animals, levelled the lowland fields.
From the coast, where the smugglers came and went,

Their pack horses moved by night through the high
passes

Of the Lakeland hills.
Season after season there was a rhythm
That the earth's inhabitants had to learn;
The swallows returning
And the silver streaks of the salmon
Fresh from the sea
Making for their birthplace
Far above the deep pools filled by the tides.
Other more frightened men
Never came out of the farther side of the fells,
But there was a fishing fleet,
And coal, along the West Cumberland coast.
The barren land
Grew a race of hardy farmers among the hills,
Tending their hardy sheep and a few cattle
In defiance of reason.

Furth of the hinterland fells
There was so called civilisation,
The more curious of the intelligentsia
Were drawn by the poems that Wordsworth wrote
Until the August hills were filled.
Schoolmasters with alpenstocks,
Dressed in tweed plus-fours,
And university dons
Smoking incessant pipes.
Two wars later the young men were taken away
To a different method of living, and wives
No longer prepared to milk cows
In the stalls of the byre on winter mornings.
Those who were left
Were not prepared to change.

So the land declined and the old industries died,
But the lakes and the hills
And the timeless surge of the sea
Survived, as year after year,
A few of the native people returned

To their roots.
Just as the silver salmon,
Just as the seeds of the birch
In the autumn wind,
Returning to the holy places of their birth,
Man, too, returns
In praise of his God, and Cumberland,
Seeking tomorrow.

*Written for a choral and orchestral work by David Challis
who shortly afterwards lost his life in tragic circumstances in
the Coniston Fells.*

For the Hungry and Afraid

Tonight in the spindrift snow
Spare a thought for the birds
And the beasts in the fields.
Think, as you sit in the warmth of your room
Of the fear in the glittering eyes
Of the sparrows
As they perch in the creeper
Watching the pencils of light
Through the curtain chinks;
Cruel wind ruffles the down
Of the doves in the spruces,
Of the hares in their forms,
Facing the merciless day of starvation.
Spare a thought,
Spare a thought for the stirring life
In the womb of the starving hind
In the drifts and the wind,
In the rocks of the eagles.
You, who are kind, will have heard the wind's whisper,
"Have pity, have pity, on the birds and the beasts,
Spare a thought, spare a prayer for their night in the
snow."

To Greenpeace and the Gentlemen of the Press from the People of West Cumberland

You sowed the seeds of doubt within our minds
And now, if I should say
"We live here, leave us be!"
You will reply to me
"You object to us stirring the waters
Only because you fear
It may destroy
The value of your property."

And if I say
"Our work is here"
You answer then
"You are afraid your jobs may go.
Your livelihood. It's we
Who know best what is good for you."

So how can we, the people win,
The people of West Cumberland,
For whom, in midst of mass hysteria
You do not really care?
It's we you have caught in the endless web
Which you have made.
We are not dogmatic,
But many of us do believe
The future of the world
Must lie with cheaper, cleaner, energy -
Atomic power.
We are not careless of the growing child,
The foetus in the mother's womb.
It really isn't so,
For we, like you,
Care deeply for the human race,
And birds, and fish, and suffering -
About our future in the doubtful world.

All I can do is quote to you
The words which Cromwell spoke
To the Commissioners of the General Assembly,

Of the Church of Scotland.
"Gentlemen, I beseech you, by the bowels of Christ,
Consider that you may be mistaken."

Tonight, I know I speak
For many of the people of West Cumberland.
We do not feel the threat
You tell us lies within our lives
Along the coast from Sellafield.
We only wish you'd go -
Back to the roaring south,
To cigarettes and petrol fumes,
Which kill you much, much quicker
Than all the things you try to make us fear
From nuclear power.
One time
You did a useful job and pointed out
Matters that needed put to rights.
But now it seems you will let no one win
Unless they can agree with you.

The people of West Cumberland
Say "Go!"
Please leave us be.

Ron Greer

Hush for the boy
Who three and forty years ago
Was born among the Glasgow streets.
From early youth his Grandad taught
Him how to catch the sticklebacks
In city pools. He went
To college and he spent his holidays
Hitchhiking up the country roads
With bags of trees
Upon his broadening back,
Planting them here and there

Across the Scottish countryside.
For all the city bred gentility he met
His tongue was sometimes rather rough,
But then the tasks he set himself
He did through love, knowing instinctively
That what he did was right.
Tonight
I watched him striding out
Across the mountain dusk.
He wandered off, a fox, all rusty red,
Reflection of the setting sun,
As though he wished to jump
Across the evening star.
His woolly bonnet on his rusty head,
His spade across his shoulder,
He looked so competent
Among the growing trees he'd taught
His friends to plant for twenty years.
So now
The rowan tree across the rising moon
Is testament to all the ethics of the man
Who dreamed those trees
Among the mountain wilderness
Which has become his home.

Ron Greer is a man whose heretical views suit neither modern convention nor modern authority, not that fear of either could moderate his powerful eccentricity. From boyhood, when his grandfather taught him to catch sticklebacks in the back streets of Glasgow, his interest took him to work at the Freshwater Fisheries Laboratory at Faskally where he acquired his knowledge of Arctic Char and his dedication to cannibal trout.
In his youth he was to be found in his spare time hitchhiking up the roads of Scotland with bags of trees on his back, planting them at random on countless verges. For his work with the Loch Garry Tree Group he won The Times Conservation Award.

Sally Ann's Wedding

If I were an eagle,
As a present to you
On your wedding day,
Out of my wing I would pluck
One feather,
Hoping for you
That its gift would give
All the wonder of flight;
Hoping that you, as I,
Might find the use
Of the swirling wind in the hills
Through your pinions,
Learning to fly.
I would wish you might share
With the mate you have found,
The beauty of places unknown
To anyone else but me,
For there is no gift in the whole wide world
Greater than this
That could ever be mine to give.
This, and the sound of the waves
Of the Island seas.

This feather of mine
I would give
With the wish to you both
That soon you might learn to see with my piercing eyes -
To sweep through the blue of the mountain sky
With the power of my wings
To the places where I
Have been happy.

I shall say a prayer on your wedding day.
Wishing the wish that may bring you at last
To the finding of peace
And the love of a caring man.
This, and my feather
Is all that I have to give -
This, and the thought of the sound
Of the Island Seas.

Gordon Arms – Herds' Dinner

I well remember
How I came along this road
The day that war broke out
In 1939.
Grandmother had the shooting
Of the grouse at Elibank.
My cousin shot a salmon
In the Tweed
(not quite, do you think?!)
While I
Was hauled across the hottest coals
For taking the equivalent of rubber rings
To a statue in the garden
With a well-aimed shot from my .22!
Aged 9, we were,
A very original sin!
Later, one day in spring, I came,
With a woman I loved - love still,
The snow was melting
On the highest tops
We picked a hazel twig
With catkins on
From a bush that stood
On a primrose bank
Above the road
That runs beside the burn
Which rushes down
From Megget Head.
We watched a kestrel
While we walked and talked.
She's kept the twig
For more than twenty years.

For thirty springs I herded sheep.
Like you I had my favourites.
Like you, I'm sure, I've had my share
Of rough delinquent ewes
Who disappeared at lambing time,
Raking across the best-kept dykes -
And eating state-owned trees.

Patrick of the Hills

It's wonderful the way it runs
In families (I have 4 daughters
Just as wild as me -
I ought to know!
We none of us conform!)

There was one ewe I had,
She must have come, I think,
From somewhere near the Tinnis March.
I bought her at a sale
Among a motley lot
Out of a Cheviot ewe, she was,
Got on a day
The Minstrel, peeping through the dyke,
Fancied her mother's chalk white face,
Escaped John's eagle eye, he did,
Just long enough to do
What £14,000 of Blackface tup
Was never meant to do,
A hundred and twenty-nine ewes, he'd had,
McClymont's very best,
But oh! The bonny whitefaced ewe
Was more than he could bear to miss,
The fertile brute, he was!

My sheep, she had two spikey horns,
And two lambs every year;
A funny speckled face, she had,
That neither parent would have owned -
Nor John!
I called her plain Carnegie then,
Kept her for seven years or more.
She killed a fox -
Even more certainly
Than Alan Kerr.
I had my stick around her neck, one day.
Careering like Ferrari cars
Around the close, we went,
But she, she had the brakes to match
And I went shooting like a star
Across the top of Paddy Slacks.

I cut my nose.
I grazed my chin,
And lost a tooth or two -
And swore!

From then till now
I have avoided
The road that runs
To Yarrowford
Past Tibby Shields,
In case, like Minstrel,
I'm seduced
By some loose lady ghost
That still patrols
The edges of the Tinnis march.
But that's not all!
One of Jim Wilson's dogs, I had.
We worked together fourteen years.
The day she came
The man who had her
Beat her and said
She wouldn't work.
I took her home.She was intelligent.
She took a fancy to the office chair
And chose a book to tear to shreds,
"Competitive Farming", it was called.
I, who have lived on subsidy
Since 1959
Perfectly understood!
Sometimes
She was deaf as a post,
And that my youngest daughter tells me
Was how my children
Learnt to swear.
Otherwise we were
A quite efficient pair!

Politicians come and go,
But animals don't let us down.
All that is left for me to do
Is wish

Patrick of the Hills

That April may come soon again
With plenty milk for plenty lambs.
And when the tup sale's past again
I hope enough is left to buy
A dress to tell your wife you love her.
If not,
Like me, you'll have to do
With hazel catkins that you'll find
Beside the burn that rushes yet
From Megget Head to Mary's loch.
So raise your glass
And drink with me
To Scotland's dogs
And Scotland's men.
Remember the sheep who've kept you,
The ones who've made you louping mad
And when you're ghosts
Among the hills
Never forget the Scottish land
For it will have the last laugh yet.

Letter From Orkney

Everybody's gone.
How can I tell you what it's like,
All this meeting of the skies and the seas,
And the deep rhythms of the tide:
And the wanting to tell,
And meeting of past and present in a single rainbow arch
With the boat lying at anchor in the sparkled waters
Of Fersness Bay.

Alone, at last,
With nothing but the thought of you for company.

How can I paint for you
The silver second's space,
With the sun, and the deep blue of the sea,
The white sands, and eroded cliffs,
And the silent ship swinging in the bay.

Even as the dream of your arms
Around me in the quiet night,
Eday lies green about me,
Its well set-up houses with the great slabs of slate
On the roof trees,
A field of turnips, and the tardy corn
Still not in ear.
A horse grazes on the headland.
I see the heather tops of Rousay,
And the fitty Hill of Westray to the northwest,
Where the clouds are piled white
Above the coloured sea.

The grass fields around the deserted houses
Of Faray lie beside me.
On Faray, now, only cows and sheep graze
Where once there were people,
And all the doors have been removed.

I watched the diamond waters, reflected in the glass
Of the boat's windows, deeply conscious of the Viking
songs
Of centuries ago, and the strain of the blood of the people
Who dropped down from them into the twentieth
century.
I can hear the lap of their oars at the top of the Sound,
As I heard their laugh in the paved streets of Stromness.
"The cleverest men in the Western Ocean"
So they had written on the walls of Maeshowe Cairn.
And "Ingevor is fairest of them all",
But I am listening, only for you,
Only for your voice in the stillness of the isles.
Now the young ones go away to school in Kirkwall.
The English come to farm the fields of Egilsay
Without understanding.
Somewhere there's a generation missing out of this land,
And the people who do understand are getting old.
They are the survivors, struggling with the tantrums
Of ill-tempered weather.
They do not really want to go away,
But the young ones go, and the people who come in their
place

Patrick of the Hills

Do not have skills of survival and independence which
The inhabitants of these isles have always needed
Since the days when the Viking jarls
Lay anchored in the bay.

Yesterday I went to Shapinsay
And talked to the men up at the Showfield.
Many of the farms are cutting their breeding cattle by a
third.
There isn't enough fodder anywhere. It's rained for
thirteen months.
The silage machines stand bogged in the fields.
At last there's sun.
Now it's too late.
What can I do, my love?
I broadcast on the wireless for thirty minutes
To try to cheer them on,
And they say thank you, but I know
From talking to the bank,
And George Muir at the auction mart,
That for many, whatever I can do,
Spring will bring disaster.

Last night I was in Rousay,
Dancing with the children at the Flower Show dance.
Reo Ritchie took us to Trumland,
Lent us a Landrover,
And gave us gin.
I poured it in the flowers, when he wasn't looking,
A tumblerful completely neat.
In the morning we had fresh fish,
And I walked among the fuschia hedges on the hill,
And the flowers in the gin were dead.

Now I am by myself,
Anchored in the silver bay,
Alone at last with my thoughts
And you.
Oh! My love what would happen if I sat back
And did nothing, and stopped worrying about these
people

Would life be different in this lovely place?

Would life be different?
Or are the forces of economics and ignorance
Of governments something so inevitable
That I am wasting my whole life?

You do not believe it, do you?

Somehow it gives me courage to think that,
Because I'm not going to give up,
When I see farms grow bigger and bigger.
And the red of their bank statements,
Like a crimson sunset.

Life is about people,
And I mind about these people,
Somehow, doubly, because of you.

In the morning back to Kirkwall and the Dounby Show.
Tomorrow I shall buy you a birthday present
In the silver factory. Later back to Stromness.

Soon, in a week or two,
I shall come back to you,
Back out of the strange land
Where the sea and the skies are one,
And the whole world echoes with the noise of the tide
And the seabirds' crying;
But tonight, when I hear the slap, slap of the waves
Against the boat
In the deserted harbour at Whitehall,
Where every second house in the village is empty
Since the herring fleet left,
I shall reach along the moonpath
And fold you in my mind with the thought
Of Eday, and the dappled waters of the sunlit Sound.

Hen Pheasant in a Hampshire Syndicate

Hazel on hazel,
The tap of the beaters' sticks in the rides;
Rustle of leaves,
And the slavering mouths of the dogs
Follow the scent where the pheasants fed
On the acorns under the trees;
And the eight men waiting,
Sitting on hickory sticks,
Or standing, with twenty-six inches of steel
Tucked under their arms,
Taking their Saturday ease in the field
At the edge of the woods on a Hampshire farm.
Surely just one of them,
Purging his week's pursuits in the city streets,
Must have felt a small fractional part
Of the fear in the heart
Of the bird, crouched low in the briars,
Not understanding.

Not understanding
How the hand of the man who had fed it from birth,
Fed it even the morning before,
Could suddenly tip up the world,
Making it fly for life,
High, high into the sun, over the trees,
Out of the arms of shelter and over the guns,
For the pattern of pellets to sever
The flesh from the bone, and fracture the tendons,
And horribly maim.

Is there not one of the eight who can feel
A little of pain himself,
As he watches reproach in the terrified amber eye
In the stalks of the stubble;
Watches the blood-matted feathers,
And the bare white tendons,
And the set of the fluttering wing?
Is there not one of the eight
Who can feel

Just the tiniest tremor of fear
As he sits on his hickory stick
With his twenty-six inches of steel
Tucked under his arm?

Berit

Wild the night
And the trough of the fierce sea
Black beneath us
Under the high wall of the waves.
Tossed are their creamy crests
Like the manes of a thousand horses
Galloping in the gale.
Storm breaking,
Over our galley's prow
And the oarsmen
Powerless in the arms of the storm.
We sailed from our home,
Place of the cattle-filled fields
And the smiling firth
On the day before the day before
Yesterday.
Farewell to our homes
Standing on the silent shore
In the middle of evening
Great in its stillness
Over the silver sea,
The hills of our kinsmen
Dark behind us
In the grief of our absence.

Far into the ocean
We met the gale of our fears.
If this wind continues
We shall surely celebrate
The coming of morning
In the hall of our fathers.

Patrick of the Hills

All I can see
Is the terrified face of my men
But even now
In the eyes given to me
By my mother of the second sight
Is the seeing of Berit
A light through the darkness,
Calling me on, leading me on
Through the fury of the storm,
To the peace of her arms, and my longing.
Her blessing sits in my eyes,
Her blessing within me.

I know that at dawn
The wind will back to the west;
And the voice of the seabirds cry once more
Around the heads of my sailors
Like the lonely call
Of my life's longing.
Then will the shout of my voice
Echo across the dawn in its clearness.
Heave ho! Boys and raise the sail!
Set the prow eastwards
Into the morning sun
With the wind fair at our backs.
Four days from now
We shall enter the shelter of the long fjords
Far from the call
Of the night's terror,
Coming home to my life's beginning.
Coming home to my life's beginning,
Swift as the salmon,
Certain as the salmon
Returning to the rivers of their birth.
We shall reach quite soon to the place
Of the wooden house,
To Berit of the Smiling Eyes,
Haunting my life.
Leading me through the wildness;
Berit of the smiling eyes,
Whose hand I shall always need,

Leading me to safety
Through the fury of a thousand storms
Berit of my longing,
Berit of the thousand dreams.

The Crossing of the Waters

I know that the wild swans
Will take me home tonight,
Take me home to the west,
Beyond the hills of my longing
Through the Window of Corrarder.

The silent snow falls thick
In great pure flakes
Among the needles of the pines
And I am tired tonight
And would have rest.

I have always fought hard
For what I believed to be right
But now suddenly I feel sick of fighting
And sure only
That I must go home tonight.

For I have heard the pulse
Of the whoopers' wings
Forcing their pinions through the gale
Laying their yellow beaks
Above the slapping waves.

Where I am to go I do not know,
But trust the wild white birds
And I
Will rest awhile, my love,
For them - and you.

Time to Go Home

I stand four square,
Imprisoned as the Romans were,
Within the granite circle of these unforgiving hills -
They hold me in their grip,
Limp as a hare, inert,
With no ambition left, except to wish
The end may come as swift as once I was,
Without the penalty of too much pain.

Others have stood where I now stand
As victim of their different circumstance.
For many this may be their home,
But not for me,
Who knew so short a time ago
The wind among more generous hills,
The freedom of the island sea.

I would go back to find myself,
But know deep down
That it may never be;
That here perhaps I have to die,
Aware of life that lies beyond this prison place,
Knowing quite well
The north point in the night time sky.

Until my final breath is gone
All I can do is pray
That when the spring returns,
Breaking the buds along the branch tips of the trees
The greylag geese may take me home
Within the phalanx of their beating wings,
To find a place to be at peace,
Somewhere beyond the Hebrides.

At Parting

When you are old, my love
If I can learn to fly
On the back of an eagle
Into the farthest sky,
Perhaps you will know
And look
For the speck in the heavens,
That looks always for you,
And learn to wave
Your handkerchief.

For LMA

My sweet,
In little more than four years space
I've watched you grow from child to womanhood.
I've seen you on the lawn at Holyrood
The day we went to see the Queen,
And typing letters from the scripts I wrote
That only you, in all the world,
Could ever learn to read.
Through all those days, and weeks, and years
I learnt to know and trust
That anything I told you would be safe.
When most I needed courage you were always there,
Cheering me on at moments when I've had to go
On far, far journeys to some distant place,
And that is why, so often
In hills and islands as I pass,
Sometimes by day, sometimes by night,
Your eyes are constant in my mind
Helping me understand
Why I must still continue to the end
Seeking a better future for
The people in the distant glens
Of my beloved land.
Turning my silver to the moon that's new

Patrick of the Hills

Each night I wish
That through my constant thoughts
You, too, may one day find
The beauty of the sights I store
Behind my gleaming eyes - for you,
For you, my sweet,
Who, through the years that we've been friends,
I've watched with love,
Growing from child to womanhood.

*Lorraine Alexander, honorary goddaughter. Personal assistant
to the Director of the Scottish Landowners' Federation.*

Fool's Gold

I do not know
What seems to grip the minds of young America -
The frantic search for excellence,
Ambition to be rich,
But riches never brought security.
They have the need to always win,
These young Americans,
But still they seem to quite forget
That dollars hardly ever bring
More than a transitory happiness.
They always need to have a bigger, better home
And swap the wives they have -
To patronise the men who live more modestly.
This is no way to live you know
The board outside my house
Says "Not for sale".

From the Beginning of the End

I no longer care for the heritage
Except in so far as the people and the circumstance
Which created it are part of the past

From which I too have come.
My care is for the land and the people
And their hope for the future.
It is no longer of use
To look continually over our shoulders
At the long road of history
That has led us to now.
We must turn our eyes to tomorrow
Instead of trying to recreate the past.

Sitting here on a Sunday morning
Beside the loch, I know I am lucky
To have been able for forty years
To draw on the spirit
Which these hills have given me,
But today I must go away to another place
To try to learn how to translate the present
Into the future.
I am under no illusions. The road
Will be full of jagged stones,
But the past is valueless
Save as a staging post on the road
And a lesson which is learnt, often badly.

Nobody can take away
The sound of the wind in the trees
Or the sun on the autumn hills.
Nobody can teach me to forget
The waves on this shore.
They are here in my mind
And neither they, nor the memory
Of the people in this place,
Can be taken away from me.
Wherever I go they are part
Of my moving, but I must stop
Thinking of the tortured past.
I can't turn back, mustn't look back,
For houses are no memorial
For someone as wild as a hawk.
Nothing stands still ever,
Not even the love of a man

For a woman.
Their separateness can never grow
Totally together in the same way.
If they are lucky their shadows may coincide
But this countryside is part of me,
Yesterday, today and tomorrow.
My love is for this land - even in hell!

Raison d'Etre - European Union

We did not starve and did not understand.
The bands along the Viennese streets
And the marching soldiers of the Reich
With their officers riding polished horses at their head.
"Sieg heil" the people cried.
The crowds cheered at the passing army
And then they broke the windows
On Krystallnacht. Broke them
Through Austria and Germany and the Sudentenland.
Peace in our time indeed! The Prime Minister
Of Britain returned from Munich
With the greatest lie in history,
So the people of Europe went to war
And nobody could save Germany from itself.

Near here where I write in Brussels,
On May 10th 1940
Parachutes were falling like blossom petals
From the spring skies and the Belgian Air Force
Was destroyed on the ground.
My friend, Thierry d'Huarth was hunted by the Gestapo.
Norway went. Denmark went. Holland went.
Luxembourg went,
And the British were in full retreat to the coast.
The French army was broken.
There were Nazi tanks in the streets,
And impending starvation.

Too many families never to see their children again;
Cattle trucks of human beings rolling eastwards to hell;
The roads blocked with refugees and broken carts,
And the whole of mainland Europe
Facing the years and years of death
Dropping out of the lovely skies.
The land occupied and the people starving.
Did God forget, for if he did,
Then we should not.

Some of us who came in 1997
Vaguely sceptical were maybe not convinced
Of the mechanics of what we saw -
The heavy weight of time on all decisions;
The need for manoeuvre to achieve consensus
To satisfy electorates in fifteen different capitals;
The lingering of national pride.
Despite all that, perhaps, we shall return to London
If not convinced, at least
More than a little impressed
By the quality and messianic zeal
Of the people we have met.
The economic arguments for union
Will no doubt rage until the last economist is dead,
But at least we can now understand
It is fear of a past nobody wants to repeat
Which is the engine driving the nations
Towards tomorrow.

Walk a little down the street, my friends,
And I will show you where a young man showed me
yesterday
His father's mother's grave.
He thought I did not understand.
In 1943, starving, she had been shot in the back
By an officer trained to kill,
Who thought she was stealing - a turnip.

So now do you understand?